Chief Martin J. Sampson of the Swinomish tribe translated chants, interpreted carvings, and explained Indian dances to outline each legend for this book.

# LONGHOUSE LEGENDS

## Emerson N. Matson

*illustrated by*

*Lorence Bjorklund*

THOMAS NELSON & SONS

*This book
is dedicated with love
to my children,
William Brock,
Robert Emerson,
and Mariellen Kay*

# CONTENTS

# Introduction

The longhouse was more than just winter living quarters for early Puget Sound Indians. It provided the space to negotiate peace with hostile tribes, was the seat of local government, served as the town hall, and played an important role in preserving family and tribal traditions.

Telling legends was the traditional way of teaching younger generations religion, tribal customs, and family history. Some stories were told by parents to their children and kept family secrets, while others were dramatized in chant and dance around the longhouse fire pits. Often, figures carved into the cedar pillars of both large and small longhouses were the only tangible record kept of these legends.

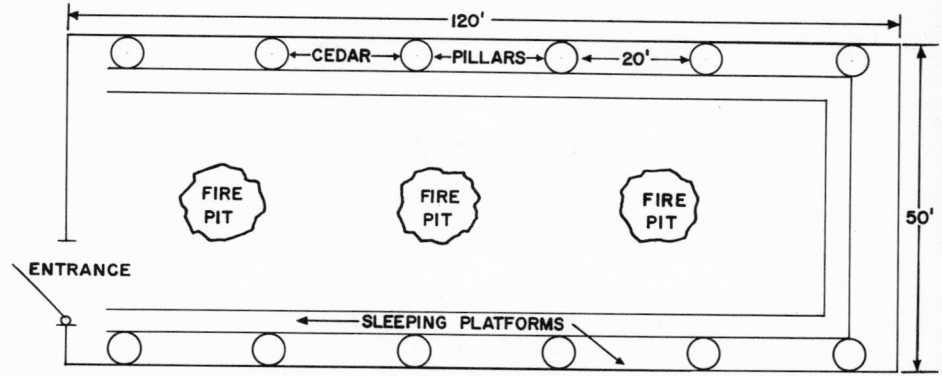

Floor Plan of Tulalip Longhouse

This longhouse at Tulalip is an exact replica of the old Snohomish Mission Creek Longhouse. A double row of raised platforms served for sleeping and sitting. Above these were shelves for storage. The ridge pole was 24 feet above the ground. On the cedar pillars supporting the roof were carved the legendary guardian spirits of the tribe.

As white settlers took over the land, massive clearing operations took place. If the cedar logs used in many of the smaller village longhouses couldn't be salvaged for fence posts or shakes, the old structures were burned along with brush and stumps.

The longhouse carvings that were common in

the 1870s are now a rarity. As the old long-houses fell victim to dry rot or clearing fires, many of the carvings that recorded the tales of past eras were lost. One of the last original long-houses was located at Tulalip, but by 1924, only an uncarved post remained.

Puget Sound Indians were excellent house builders. The first pioneers were surprised to find them living in gabled houses with split-cedar shake roofing and cedar-plank siding.

Some structures were one to two hundred feet long and, during the winter months, housed many families. When summer came, the Indians became nomadic, following fish runs or moving from area to area in search of ripening berries, edible plants, and game. During this time they usually lived in teepees.

Construction of the longhouse was a group effort. Each pillar, plank, and board, including roofing, was tied into place with hand-braided cedar-bark rope. Mats woven from cattail leaves

served as partitions dividing the family areas and protecting them from cold drafts. When a potlatch or gathering was planned, the partitions were removed to make one large room.

The housing of potlatch celebrations was an important function of the longhouse, for the potlatch was a vital part of the social life of the Puget Sound Indians. The giving of gifts, speech making, feasts, and dancing were a few of the highlights of potlatch activities. When the longhouse was large enough, friendly tribes would be invited to participate. Those attending would bring their entire family, and children would join the festivities by chanting and acting out a legend. "The Witch and Her Four Sons" was one of the legends that was popular among the young dancers.

Swinomish Chief Martin J. Sampson, who was born one year before Washington State was admitted to the Union, remembers taking part in potlatches and chanting the legends as a child, and each legend in this book was outlined by

him. Some of the chants he remembered from longhouse gatherings of seventy years ago. Others he translated from chants recalled by other old-timers on the Swinomish and Tulalip Reservations.

In 1930, Martin Sampson was named a chief before 500 tribesmen assembled on the Swinomish Reservation for the ceremony. At that time, he promised to maintain the tribal traditions, legends, and language as a part of his accepting the honor.

This he has done, and he is considered to be an authority on Puget Sound Indian language, history, and treaty rights. Chief Sampson has discussed Indian affairs with former President Harry S. Truman and Senator Warren G. Magnuson and has been the subject of a television documentary. Because of his knowledge of the language and tribal customs, on occasion he has worked at the University of Washington as a teacher of native Indian languages.

A few of the legends found in this collection

are carved on a totem-like storypole at the Swinomish Reservation. In 1938, the various tribes now making up the reservation joined in a common effort to carve a 61-foot cedar log into a modern storypole. By undertaking such a project, Chief Sampson felt, they could record their history and save it for future generations. An American eagle, carved in detail, perches on top of the monument. The image of Franklin D. Roosevelt is directly beneath, because he signed the reorganization bill that gave reservation Indians self-government. Glancing down the pole, a number of toads, bears, blackfish, and other spirit-guide symbols attracts the eye. At the base of one side of the pole is a carved likeness of Princess Ko-Kwalawoot, the Maiden of Deception Pass. On the opposite base is the figure of the boy who created the magic robe.

Just as the Swinomish Reservation tribes of the Skagit River basin built a storypole to remind youngsters of their heritage, the Tulalips

in Snohomish County have constructed a replica of their original longhouse to show how their ancestors lived. The new longhouse will have utility value too as it will be the site of intertribal meetings of Puget Sound Indians.

Some present-day Indians still live on the various reservations dotting the area. Their occupations vary and include most types of employment. However, over the years, a number have been lured by the jobs and conveniences available in metropolitan areas. When they leave their reservations to integrate into the surrounding society, they leave the traditional family and tribal legends behind, for, on the outside, the Indians find their fellow citizens unimpressed by spirit-guided fishing, hunting, or healing talents.

Thus the legends preserved through the years were passing away with the people who told them without the benefit of a written record. This book is an attempt to save a small portion of that diminishing culture for all to enjoy.

# The Maiden of Deception Pass

*The Samish Indian tribe, now living on an eleven-tribe*
*reservation near the mouth of the Skagit River*
*in northern Washington State, attributes their good*
*fishing and prosperity to the gift of the beautiful*
*maiden of Deception Pass.*
*This story was originally chanted while tribal*
*dancers acted out the highlights to the beat of a tom-tom.*
*By 1930, the words of the chant had nearly passed*
*into extinction, and only a few old-timers*
*could outline the story.*
*Chief Sampson credits the late Charlie Edwards with*
*saving the legend by carving an image of*
*Princess Ko-Kwalawoot on the Swinomish Reservation*
*storypole. Edwards, whose Samish ancestors were*
*famous for wood carving and canoe making, directed*
*the making of the pole in 1938.*
*Now the Samish pass the legend on to their children*
*as a family ritual. They believe that as the currents flow*
*back and forth through Deception Pass,*
*Princess Ko's long hair may be seen drifting with*

*the tide. The Samish say she will always be there*
*to look out for the welfare of her people.*
*She is their guiding spirit.*

# The Maiden of Deception Pass

Long before the first pioneers carved settlements out of the wilderness, and even before the first buck deer grew antlers, a beautiful Samish Indian princess named Ko roamed the beaches of Deception Pass.

It is said that Ko's long hair was blacker than charcoal and her eyes browner than the bark of the tallest fir tree. The story of her great beauty soon spread throughout the land, from the top of the tallest mountain to the bottom of the sea.

Samish Indians were known as fish eaters because the sea furnished them with most of their food. While men caught salmon and bottom fish, it was the duty of tribal maidens to dig clams and collect shellfish from the beach.

One day, after the maidens had gathered shellfish, Princess Ko was helping wash the

*Farther and farther into the current Princess Ko waded.*

catch at the water's edge. Suddenly one of the shellfish slipped from her hand and slid into deeper water.

She tried to retrieve it, but it slipped from her grasp again and again, edging each time into deeper water. Soon Princess Ko found she was in water well over her waist.

As she turned back to the beach, a large hand rose from the sandy bottom and grasped hers firmly, preventing her escape. The princess was terrified as the swift waters of Deception Pass swirled around her body, and she fought to free herself. But the powerful hand would not loosen its grip.

A voice coming from beneath the surface of the water instructed her not to struggle or be afraid. "I'm the son of the great spirit of the sea," the voice gently told Princess Ko. "You are more beautiful than all the skies. I am holding your hand only to admire your great beauty."

On the condition that she would visit him often, the spirit son released her hand. Princess Ko kept the promise and met him many times. During each meeting the spirit son spoke soothingly to her, holding her hand longer and longer. He told her of the many beautiful things that were in the sea, and finally he asked the princess to be his bride.

"Only my father can give me in marriage," Princess Ko explained.

"Then I will go to the shelter of your father and ask for your hand," the spirit son replied. He emerged from the water and followed Princess Ko to the Samish village.

As he walked through the village, people stared at the stranger who had eyes like a fish and skin covered with barnacles. "Can this be the future husband of our beautiful Princess Ko?" they asked.

In his presence the village detected a chill as though icy winds were blowing. "Surely this

creature must be from the spirit world," the people whispered as he passed.

Her father was angered at the thought of his beautiful daughter marrying a barnacle-covered sea spirit. He tried to dismiss the idea by saying, "No, my daughter cannot go into the sea to live with you. She would die."

"On the contrary," the sea spirit replied. "She will live." He explained that the spirits of the sea would give her eternal life and be very good to her. "I love her dearly, and I will see that no harm comes to her."

The father did not want his daughter to leave the village to live in the sea, so he finally told the spirit son his request could not be granted.

"If I cannot take the beautiful Princess Ko for my bride, I will remove the fish from the sea and place a curse on your drinking water. Your people will face both famine and drought, and many will die."

Despite the warning, the father would not

agree to the marriage. Instead he ordered the spirit son to return to the sea.

Soon there was a great scarcity of food, and the springs ran sour. Streams that had always flowed swift and clean dried up and stagnated. Children cried for food, and the elderly called for a drop of water to quench their thirst. Beaches once abundant with shellfish were soon barren. The tides that flowed over them did not leave behind a single living creature. Unless Princess Ko married the spirit son soon, the members of her tribe would all be dead.

The princess was as kind as she was beautiful. It deeply hurt her to see her people suffer, and when she could bear it no longer, Princess Ko went out into the water. Calling to the spirit son, she begged him to give her tribe food and water.

He replied, "Tell your father that only when you are my bride will the fish again swarm into the waters. Then your people may live in plenty once more."

She told her father of this meeting and of what the spirit son had said. Her father then realized that the only way the tribe could be saved was for him to give up his beautiful daughter.

That evening he walked to the beach and looked over the boiling waters of Deception Pass. Suddenly the image of the spirit son appeared, giving the father a cold chill.

With a heavy heart he agreed to give his daughter's hand in marriage, but only after making one stipulation. The spirit son was to allow the princess to return to the tribe for a visit once each year so that they could see if she were happy and well. This was agreed upon.

After bidding farewell to her friends and family, the beautiful princess wrapped her wedding garments around her and walked into the water. Farther and farther into the current she waded until only her hair could be seen drifting with the tide.

Almost instantly the springs bubbled pure sweet water and the streams flowed clear. The sea teemed with hordes of silvery salmon, and once again the beaches were covered with shellfish. The gifts of the sea returned, bringing prosperity to the tribe.

For four years, Princess Ko visited her people once a year as she had promised. The day before she was to arrive there was always more food than usual. But each time Princess Ko returned to visit her people, the tribe noticed a great change in her. First her hands were covered with barnacles, then her arms, and the last time she came the barnacles covered her face, which once had been so beautiful.

In her presence, people felt chilled as if icy winds were blowing. Her father noticed she seemed to be unhappy out of the sea, so, on her fourth visit, he released her from her vow to return to her people each year.

Today, as the currents flow back and forth

through Deception Pass, her hair may still be seen drifting with the tide. It is said she will always be there to look out for the welfare of her people.

# The Boy and
# His Magic Robe

*To the early Indians of the Swinomish and
Kikiallus tribes, "The Boy and His Magic Robe" was
more than a story about a wayward boy.
Parents taught their children this legend as a part
of their childhood education. They believed
it served several useful purposes.
The early members of these tribes claimed to be the
original Puget Sound Indians. Relating this legend
to their youngsters served to perpetuate this
belief, and, at the same time, explained the origin
of the neighboring tribes.
The legend also taught the children that breaking tribal
law led to complete rejection and that successes
attained during a period of punishment
would be nullified. Also, it warned youngsters
that parents have ways of finding out
about the misdeeds of their offspring.
Chief Sampson first heard this legend from his
mother in about 1893, then later from Swinomish tribal
chiefs. The story was recited, not sung or chanted.*

*The Swinomish Indians have the image of*
*Twu-Yaletsa, the boy who created the magic robe,*
*and his little dog carved on the base of*
*the reservation storypole. As a result,*
*this legend is still widely known and told*
*among the members of the tribe today.*

# The Boy and His Magic Robe

When the world was still young and only one Indian tribe occupied all of the Puget Sound country, there was a boy called Twu-Yaletsa who was the son of the Swinomish chief.

Twu-Yaletsa was not considered an evil boy, but he had one bad fault that distressed his father and the Swinomish tribe. Every day the boy would kill small animals and birds, taking only their skins or feathers and leaving the meat to waste. He stored the feathers and pelts in a small box he kept hidden near the beach.

His father warned him many times against wasteful killing. "The animals and birds are our friends, and you must not kill them except for food," his father told him. "Obey this rule or great evil will befall you!"

Because he continued to slaughter little ani-

mals, Twu-Yaletsa lost all of his friends except a small dog and a crow. When he walked through the village, many of the Indians turned their backs to him. Others whispered, "Stay away from Twu-Yaletsa, he kills without purpose."

The chief was determined to make his son obey the tribal rules. "This killing has got to stop! We will teach that boy a lesson," he announced to the people.

The next day, after Twu-Yaletsa had gone off to hunt, his father ordered the entire tribe to load their possessions into canoes. Then they paddled off to build a new village where the boy could not find them.

Twu-Yaletsa's friend the crow flew to the new village and pleaded with the father to send a canoe for the boy. But the father refused, saying, "I have spoken! The boy must be punished."

Returning to the old village, the crow buried the boy's box of skins and some coals from a fire

deep into the sand. Then the crow tied Twu-Yaletsa's small dog near the place where the skins and coals were buried.

When Twu-Yaletsa returned, he found the village deserted. Not even a hot coal could be found. He needed a cheerful fire for cooking and for protection from the cold winds blowing in from the waters of Puget Sound.

Twu-Yaletsa called to his dog, and the faithful animal answered by barking and whining. The boy ran to the animal. Overjoyed with his find, Twu-Yaletsa untied his little dog. But the dog barked and whined, as if it had something to tell the boy. Digging and scratching into the sand, the little animal soon uncovered the hot coals and the box of skins.

Twu-Yaletsa gathered sticks from the beach and piled them into a stack. Placing the hot coals in the center, he started a fire. Now the boy could roast shellfish and enjoy the heat from the flames.

Although his stomach was full and his body

warm, Twu-Yaletsa was very lonely. Only his faithful little dog remained by his side, but the animal could not talk.

As Twu-Yaletsa sat gazing at the sky, a spirit voice instructed him to make a robe from the skins stored in the box. Using a pointed bone for a needle and strips of skin for thread, the boy worked far into the night.

The final stitches in place, Twu-Yaletsa was admiring his work when the spirit voice spoke again. "You have done a fine job of sewing," the voice told him. "If you wave your robe four times over the fire, you will be lonely no longer."

The boy, eager to end his loneliness, jumped to his feet and passed his robe over the fire. With the fourth pass of the robe, the flames became very bright.

Suddenly people emerged from the smoking coals, and soon Twu-Yaletsa had a tribe of his own. The new people were hard workers, and

*Suddenly people emerged from the smoking coals.*

they kept the boy well-supplied with food and firewood. They also loved to talk and Twu-Yaletsa was lonely no longer.

One day his friend the crow flew over the camp and learned that the boy had a tribe of his own. "Ah-ha!" he said. "The boy Twu-Yaletsa has withstood the elements to become his own chief. I must tell his father of this great success."

Winging his way into the Swinomish camp, the crow screamed out, "Twu-Yaletsa is a great chieftain! Twu-Yaletsa is a great chieftain!"

"Shoot the bird down," the father told one of the warriors. "It speaks falsehoods."

But before the warrior could draw an arrow, the crow flapped down and perched near the chief. "I speak the truth," the crow assured him. "Twu-Yaletsa has a large tribe of his own."

"Where would he find people?" the father asked. "All the people are right here, with me."

The crow told the chief that Twu-Yaletsa had made a magic robe by sewing some pelts together. When the robe was waved over the

fire four times, people walked out of the burning coals to form his tribe.

Hearing that his son had created a tribe with a magic robe, the chief became very angry. He ordered all his warriors into war canoes, and they set out to conquer the boy and destroy his new people.

When the father and his warriors landed, the boy's new people fled before them until there was no place to retreat but into the sea.

"Why have you done this, my father?" Twu-Yaletsa cried out.

"Your new people were created from the smoke of burning sticks. They must be destroyed!" the father replied.

Twu-Yaletsa pleaded for his tribe, promising that if his father allowed them to float off with the tide, he would never waste food again. The father agreed to this, and the new people were allowed to build rafts of driftwood.

Leaving with the receding tide, the waves soon separated the rafts, and they were washed

upon beaches hundreds of miles apart. At every landing a new tribe was founded, and, according to Swinomish legend, this was the origin of the many smaller tribes dotting the shores of Puget Sound.

# Legends of Witchcraft

*Indian storytellers loved to tell of matching wits with
the cruel and evil practitioners of witchcraft.
"The Coyote and the Evil Witches" is based on a myth
of the early Puget Sound Indians that at one time all
living things had a common language and
assisted each other in the struggle for survival against
the common enemy. Often the common enemy
was a village of evil witches who were blamed for
lightning, thunder, and earthquakes.
Primitive tribesmen feared these witches and were
constantly devising plans to destroy them.
Even the coyote was a victim of these evil creatures, and,
in the legend of "The Coyote and the Evil Witches,"
it is explained how the coyote's slinking manner is
the result of an encounter with witches.
"The Witch and Her Four Sons" was one of the legends
popular with children. Today, only a handful
know the chant that tells the myth of Hoybuska Disha.
Chief Sampson translated the Upper Skagit versions
of these legends, although similar renditions
of both were sung or recited by most of the Salish
speaking tribes of the Puget Sound country.*

# The Coyote
# and the Evil Witches

Near the dawn of civilization, four witches lived in the mountains overlooking the roaring Skagit River. These witches were so cruel that Indians of that time described the witch village as "the land of the evil ones."

Members of the Upper Skagit tribe attempted to drive them off the mountain many times, but each crusade ended in failure. Every time attacking warriors approached the evil village, the heavens spewed fire and roared. Forest trails were blocked by uprooted fir trees. Sometimes the ground trembled so violently that braves could not maintain their footing and were thrown to the earth. Even the most powerful warriors armed with the sharpest spears and straightest arrows could not combat the magic powers.

After each battle the witches revenged themselves by placing a curse on the attackers. The witches enjoyed casting evil spells, and even if they had no reason, they would place a curse on the Indians just to watch them suffer. By calling to the clouds, the witches could set fire to the forests with a bolt of flames shot from the heavens. This frightened the animals, and it took tribal hunters weeks to relocate deer herds and other game.

Although the curses often resulted in sickness or death, the witches did nothing to help the people. Sometimes a curse was placed upon a curse, making it doubly difficult for the tribes to survive.

It was during such a curse that the people became impatient. "How long must we tolerate the evil ones?" they asked their chiefs. "What medicine are you using to conquer the witches?"

"We must search for a new and more powerful magic," the chiefs replied.

One day a coyote approached the council of tribal chiefs. At this time, the coyote was a very proud animal. He held his head and tail high because he was considered to be the smartest animal in the world. "Let me go to the land of the evil ones," he suggested. "I will destroy the witches by outsmarting them."

"How can you overcome the power of the evil ones?" demanded the chiefs. "Many of our bravest warriors have attacked their village only to be cursed into defeat."

"I have a plan," boasted the coyote. "I shall build a pitch-wood house and set fire to it. The flames will destroy their magic."

"But how will you persuade them to enter the house?" asked the chiefs.

"You'll see! You'll see!" answered the coyote. "I'm the smartest living creature in the forest."

"The coyote is indeed the smartest and proudest animal in the forest," the chiefs agreed.

With tribal permission granted, the coyote

set out for the Cascade Mountains, where the witches lived. Instead of weapons, the coyote carried a salmon freshly caught from the river.

When he neared the evil village, one of the witches called to him to ask him why he was entering their land.

"It's so seldom that I see such beautiful witch maidens," the coyote replied, "that I walked up to have a salmon dinner with you."

The coyote started to build a lean-to shelter of pitch wood. The witches asked why the shelter was being made from pitch wood.

"The fragrance of pitch wood and the delicate flavor of salmon go well together," the witches were told. "It also looks like it might rain," the coyote added as he put the finishing touches on the shelter.

Soon the feast began. The three older witches entered the pitch-wood shelter, leaving the youngest to wait outside. According to tribal customs, maidens not yet entered into woman-

hood always waited outside until their elders finished eating.

While the older witches were eating, the coyote slipped outside, touched hot coals to the pitch wood, and then ran away as fast as he could. Soon flames covered the shelter, destroying the three evil witches.

The heat of the fire prevented the youngest witch from entering to save her sisters. As she watched the flames, she pledged to avenge their deaths.

Although she was young and her powers not yet fully developed, she called on her magic to help her trace the trail of the fleeing coyote. She followed his trail from the upper Skagit River country south across the Columbia River into Oregon, then back to the headwaters of the Columbia River.

The coyote, who was exhausted and could run no longer, had climbed into a small cave to hide.

In the cave, he kept his head close to the ground in order to listen for the approach of the witch maiden. Instead of walking about proudly, the coyote cowered, fearing he might be discovered.

The young witch found the power of her magic had been greatly reduced as a result of the long chase. Soon she would have no strength left. If she were to avenge her sisters' deaths, she must act quickly. Calling on every bit of her remaining power, the witch located the coyote's cave.

"Come out coyote!" she ordered. "Come out or I shall fill your cave with fire."

But the frightened coyote could not move.

"Hurry coyote, this is your last chance," she warned.

The coyote did not leave the cave, and he was too frightened to reply.

The witch maiden tried and tried to produce fire, but without her sisters she could not make

*"Come out, Coyote. I have food and water for you,"*
*the witch whispered into the cave*

so much as a spark. Since her power was leaving her rapidly, the witch decided to attempt treachery in order to catch the tired coyote.

"Come out, Coyote. I have food and water for you," she whispered into the cave.

The coyote, who was both hungry and thirsty after the long chase, came out. The young witch noticed how the once proud animal's head drooped and how his tail dragged.

"Ah-ha!" she told herself. "With my remaining magic I shall remove the coyote's pride forever." When he emerged from the cave, the witch cast her last spell on him. This drained so much of her energy that she died.

Thus, the coyote was doomed to slink about forever, never to regain his pride, and it is said that the power of the young witch affects the animal still.

A wood carving of Princess
Ko appears on the Samish
side of the totem pole on
the Swinomish Indian
Reservation. The totem was

Samish Indians now living on a reservation near the mouth
of the Skagit River believe that salmon will always return to
fill their beach seines because of the marriage of Princess Ko
to the spirit of the sea.

erected in 1939 as a monument to the remaining members of the tribes that were moved to the reservation by the government.

On the Swinomish side of the reservation totem pole there is a cedar carving of Twu-Yaletsa, the boy who created the magic robe, and his faithful dog.

# The Witch and Her Four Sons

Deep in the Upper Skagit country many miles from any Indian village, there once lived an old witch named Hoybuska Disha.

Hoybuska Disha was not an ordinary witch. She not only possessed many evil powers, but she had a long toenail shaped like a knife. They say her toenail was so sharp that she could cut down a sapling with the mere twitch of her toe.

Her sons were not ordinary men either. Tribal legend says they were four of the most handsome men in the world. Each stood straight as a fir tree and possessed amazing muscular strength. They could outrun the fastest deer, were successful hunters, and could catch salmon when others failed. Indian maidens from far and near admired them and prayed to be their wives.

But none admired the four sons more than the

four daughters of a medicine squaw living in a distant village. Each day, from the rising to the setting of the sun, the daughters longed to marry the four sons of Hoybuska Disha.

One night, around the cooking fire, the sisters decided that the eldest of them should approach the brothers to see if they were seeking brides. So early the next morning, the eldest girl set out to find the shelter of Hoybuska Disha. She traveled many miles through the forest until she came to a clearing. As she crossed the clearing, she sang an ancient Indian song:

> "I am a young maiden,
> A beautiful young maiden looking for the man of my dreams.
> I am a young maiden in search of a husband.
> Each step brings me closer to my brave."

The cruel witch heard the girl singing the song of love and walked out to greet her. "You are looking for my sons?" asked Hoybuska Disha.

*Hoybuska Disha heard the young girl singing and called out, "Are you looking for my sons?"*

"Oh yes," answered the maiden. "When may I meet them?"

"They are high in the mountains hunting and will not return for several days. Why don't you wait for them at my shelter?" invited the evil witch.

Once in her cedar-log hut, the witch ceased being hospitable. She made the poor girl clean and groom her hair and then ordered her to gather firewood. After there was enough wood to last the night, the witch told the girl to find some food for dinner. But the sun had set in the west, and during the last few flickering moments of daylight the maiden could find only a handful of berries. Presenting them to the witch, the girl hoped that the old woman might divide them. But Hoybuska Disha greedily devoured every last one.

"You have failed to provide me with enough food to satisfy my hunger," the witch admonished the maiden. "So I must eat your heart for my supper."

Using her long toenail as a knife, the cruel witch cut the heart out of the maiden and ate it in one bite. Then she hid the girl in a hollow cedar stump.

When the eldest daughter failed to return to her village, the remaining sisters thought she had taken her pick of the sons and forgotten to come back for them. So they dispatched the next eldest to arrange for their marriages.

The second sister traveled through the forest, and when she came to the clearing, she also sang the ancient song:

> "I am a young maiden,
> A beautiful young maiden looking for the
> man of my dreams.
> I am a young maiden in search of a husband.
> Each step brings me closer to my brave."

Then she added two new lines to the song:

> "My eldest sister married one of the witch's
> sons,
> And now I come to marry a second."

Hoybuska Disha heard her singing and called out, "Are you looking for my sons?"

"Oh yes," replied the second sister. "I hear they are the most handsome men in the world, and I wish to marry one of them."

"You must first prove yourself worthy," answered the cruel witch. "Come to my shelter, and I will give you a test to see if you will make a good wife."

But once the maiden entered Hoybuska Disha's shelter, she found the witch was no longer friendly.

"Groom and clean my hair," the witch ordered.

"But I've come a long way to meet your sons," the maiden protested. "I am hungry and would like to eat before working."

"I am hungry too," the witch snapped back and cut the maiden's heart out with her long toe-nail. "This will do for my supper," Hoybuska Disha said.

Many days later, the remaining sisters decided

that the second had also married and forgotten
them. So the third sister packed her belongings
and walked into the forest to find the sons of
Hoybuska Disha.

At the edge of the clearing, the third sister
sang the same song as her older sisters, but she
added:

> "My older sisters married two of the
> witch's sons,
>
> And now I come to marry the third."

Hoybuska Disha heard her singing and came
out to greet her. "You must be singing of marriage to my third son," the witch said. "How do
I know you will make a good wife for him?"
she asked.

"I will make a fine wife," the girl replied. "I
can gather clams and berries and carry the
heaviest pieces of firewood."

"Then you must come to my shelter, and we
will see what kind of a wife you will make,"
Hoybuska Disha answered.

Like her sisters, the third found that Hoy-

buska Disha became cruel and unfriendly once she entered her shelter.

Run out and bring in a large log for my fire," the witch demanded.

"I can carry firewood," the girl replied. "But logs are too heavy for me to carry."

"Then I must have your heart for my supper," the witch said. With one stroke of her toenail Hoybuska Disha removed the third sister's heart and then placed her body in the cedar stump.

The fourth and youngest girl grew lonely when her sisters failed to return.

"Why haven't my sisters come back with news of marriage?" she asked her mother.

The mother was known throughout the land for her wisdom and her medicine. Hers was not ordinary medicine, but a special potion that was said to be able to produce great and wonderful magic.

"We will make a strong medicine that will help guide you to the right trail, my daughter,"

the mother said. She brewed some of her most potent potion in a clam shell and gave it to the girl. After drinking it, the maiden went to bed.

Later that night, she dreamed of the evil witch Hoybuska Disha and knew that her sisters had been slain by the witch's toenail. During the dream, she saw a way to subdue the witch and revive her three sisters.

"The medicine has spoken," she told her mother upon awakening. During her journey to the hut of Hoybuska Disha, at the edge of the clearing where her sisters had sung a song of love, the youngest also sang. But her song was not of love.

> "May the strong medicine of my mother give me power,
> For I must cut the nail of Hoybuska Disha."

The witch was sound asleep when the girl arrived. Before entering the hut, she danced around the shelter three times. As she danced, she softly sang this medicine song:

"Sleep like a winter bear,
Sleep like the forest at night.
Continue to sleep,
And your wrongs I'll make right."

Then she slipped into the hut and quickly severed Hoybuska Disha's great toenail, awakening her.

"Who are you?" the witch demanded. Then she saw that her toenail was missing.

"You have destroyed my ability to cast a curse by cutting my toenail!" Hoybuska Disha cried. "You have ruined my evil powers."

"Now you can use magic only for good," the young maiden told the witch. "What have you done with my sisters?"

"Wait here, and I will bring them back with my most powerful magic," the changed witch said.

Hoybuska Disha went to the cedar stump where she had left the maiden's sisters. Using her magic for good, she was able to restore the sisters' hearts and bring them back to life.

When Hoybuska Disha's sons arrived, they were delighted to find that their witch mother was no longer evil. They swore to trim Hoybuska Disha's toenail every day, because, as long as it was short, the evil spirit could not control her magic.

The sisters and their handsome braves were soon married. They settled along the Skagit River and had many children.

# The Legend of the Star Children

*Until Christian missionaries established outposts in
Skagit County, Washington, this legend was the basis of
the law, religion, and administration of medicine
of the primitive Indians who lived along the Skagit River.
All Indian tribes had a star child legend.
Sometimes the creature that descended from the
heavens was a crow or some other animal, but, as in
the case of this Skagit translation, usually it was
a squaw and her child.
During his stay on earth, the star child told
the people many legends that would help them survive.
Two of the fables the star child brought to earth
were "The Mink and the Weasel" and
"The Mink and the Sun." Both are found
elsewhere in this book.
The Indians believed that the star child also named the
mountains and other prominent landmarks.
For example, the mountain formed by the coil
of rope in this legend is located east of Mount Vernon,*

*Washington. White settlers called it
"Big Rock Mountain," but the Indians have
their own name for it.*

# The Legend of the Star Children

At one time when the world was in its early stages, one chief ruled all the villages.

He had twin daughters who were reported to be so beautiful that every young warrior sought to marry one of them. But the sisters never consented, always hoping for even handsomer husbands to match their striking beauty.

One day when the maidens were gathering camas roots on a small prairie near Clear Lake, they worked until after sundown. Realizing that they could not make it back to their village before complete darkness descended on the prairie, the maidens lay down side by side on the ground to sleep. But as night approached and the stars covered the heavens, two stars shone brighter than the rest, and the two maidens, looking up into the sky, thought of marriage.

"The brave that receives my hand must shine as bright and beautiful as that big red star up there," one of the sisters said. "And my husband must be as bright and beautiful as that white star up there," the other replied. So saying, they dropped off into a deep slumber.

When they awoke, the sisters found that they had been swept up to the land of the stars while asleep, and soon they were married to the red and white stars as they had wished.

The girl who married White Star was delighted with her husband and thought he was as handsome as she was beautiful. But the sister who married Red Star was soon dissatisfied with her marriage.

"My husband looks tired after carrying the red starlight all night, and when he looks tired, he does not match my beauty," the girl told herself. The more she thought about this, the uglier and more disagreeable he appeared to her and the more she longed to return to earth.

One day the sisters were out digging camas roots on a prairie which looked much like the one on earth. Although they had been cautioned that deep roots were to be left and only the shallow ones uprooted, the bride of Red Star told her sister that she wanted to dig up the deepest root on the prairie.

"You must not do that, my sister!" gasped the other. "We have been forbidden to dig deep roots."

"I'm going to do it just the same," she insisted, and started to dig as rapidly as she could.

"Why are you doing it?" White Star's wife asked.

"I must see what is down below us," was the reply, and she continued to dig deeper and deeper.

Finally she called out, "Look what I've found!" The twin hurried to the hole and peered down to see the earth below them. The hole pierced the sky directly above the Skagit

country where the girls had lived before they were brought to the land of the stars.

"I'm going to use this hole to escape back to earth," the twin married to Red Star said. "I have had enough of this star life."

"But how can you?" asked her sister. "It's too far to jump."

"The spirit has given me a plan. You must help me make a rope from cedar saplings long enough to reach the earth. We can both escape on it."

"We don't have time to make a rope. We are supposed to be gathering camas roots, and besides, I don't want to leave here," said the girl married to White Star. "I love my husband very much, and I'm very fond of the star people."

"Then help me this way," her twin commanded. "Gather twice as many roots so you will have enough to cover my share, and I'll braid the rope. When it's completed you can hold one end while I climb down to earth. After

*After bidding her twin farewell, Red Star's wife slipped through the hole and slid to earth down the rope.*

I'm back on earth you can drop it down to me and fill up the hole so no one will know where I've gone."

The sisters worked long and hard for many days. When the rope was long enough, the twins selected the darkest night of the year to lower it down to earth.

After bidding her twin farewell, the sister slipped through the hole and slid to earth down the rope. When she landed, she gave the rope a tug and her twin sister let it drop. As the rope fell, it coiled neatly, forming a small mountain which turned to rock.

Walking away from the mountain of rock, the girl looked for her people. Alone in a dark forest, she became very frightened and called to her twin sister in the sky to send down spirit help.

Soon a voice told her not to be afraid and to follow instructions. She was taught how to trap fish and game, how to gather food, and how to

build a shelter in the forest. The voice warned her that she would soon be the mother of Red Star's son, and she should prepare for the birth.

After her son was born, she found it difficult to take care of the baby and go out for food and wood. She turned to the sky and asked her sister to plead with Red Star for help.

Early one evening, when she thought that both she and the star child would starve, the spirit voice returned. She was instructed to follow a forest trail to a log that was shaped like a woman. When she found it, the voice ordered her to pass her hand over the figure four times, which she did. The log came to life and promised to serve as a nurse for her star child.

Before leaving, Red Star's spirit voice warned that if anyone learned that the boy was a star child, he would be stolen. The nurse was cautioned never to reveal the fact in her songs and chants.

One day while the mother was checking her

traps, two squaws happened by. Tending traps is work for a man, and the squaws became very curious.

"What kind of a brave would let the woman trap game?" they asked each other and quietly slipped into the brush to watch.

The mother, who had not seen them, sang of her beautiful son, the child of a star. The hidden squaws longed for a boy of their own and set out to find this beautiful star child.

At the hut, the squaws found the nurse sleeping and the star child unattended. Wrapping him in a deer skin, they left undetected.

When the mother returned and found her child missing, she fell into a rage. Turning the nurse back into a rotten log, she called to Red Star for help.

"You have disobeyed orders from the heavens twice," the spirit voice told her. "You are no longer Red Star's wife, and your wish cannot be granted. You must find the star child or be severely punished."

After weeping long and bitterly, the mother wiped the tears from her cheeks and headed for the banks of the Skagit River. "Does not every living creature come to these waters for food and drink?" she asked herself. "Surely I will find my son near the river."

She searched the gravel bars and adjoining marshlands a long time before she finally found some moccasin tracks on a sandy stretch of the river bank. "Maybe these tracks will lead me to my child," she thought and began to sing songs of happiness.

But her joy suddenly turned to fear as a band of warriors rushed at her from ambush. She froze with fright when she saw that they were led by Raven, the cruel chief of a hostile tribe.

His piercing black eyes met hers and he grabbed her firmly by the arm. "Look my braves," he said, holding her up so she was on the tips of her toes. "Look at this beautiful prize I have captured. She will make a fine slave wife."

Raven was as ugly as she was beautiful, and

the thought of becoming his slave sickened her. She called to Red Star for help, but the sky remained silent.

"You will do as I say or be whipped," Raven commanded. He forced her to groom his dirty hair and cut brush for his firewood. Raven seemed to delight in whipping her and would beat her often to amuse his friends.

"If I only could escape to find my star child," she told herself daily. But the years passed, and she gave him up as lost forever.

The two squaws who had stolen the star child raised him to be a fine boy. He was different from anyone else they had ever seen because a bright light surrounded him at all times.

The star boy knew he had been taken from his mother because he often overheard the squaws laughing about it. This gave him the determination to go into the forest and search for her.

Then one day he heard a woman singing in the brush. Her song told the story of a star child,

and he knew he had found his mother.

At this moment Raven came along and asked the boy why he was watching his slave at her brush-cutting work. The boy threw a shiny shell into the air, and when Raven leaped up to catch it, he was turned into a bird of the air.

"He will bother you no more," the boy assured his mother. "From now on, Raven will be a camp pest with a harsh, scolding voice."

"You belong in the heavens with your father," the repentant mother told her boy. "The nights are long and dark, and we need someone to give us more light."

She called to Red Star to take the child into the sky to help light the world. A voice answered her request, stating he would lift the boy into the heavens, but she could not come with him as an Indian woman. The mother chose to be transformed into a small green frog so she could accompany her son, and they ascended into the land of the stars.

When they arrived, they found that the twin

sister and White Star had a son who was identical in appearance to the star child from earth. It was decided that the star child from earth should shine at night because he had been on earth and knew how dark the forests were at night.

He became the moon. His identical cousin became the sun and promised to shine all day.

The little green frog lives with the moon, and the image of a frog can be seen on the face of the moon to this day.

# The Raven and the Crow

*This legend, translated from a chant, was used primarily
by children to entertain adults attending
a potlach. As the adults sat around the longhouse
fires, the children would chant and dramatize the
story of Raven and Crow.
It was a legend popular with both adults and children
and was used at potlaches by most tribes in the
Puget Sound area. To the Indian, these potlach
dramatizations were equivalent to the theater of today.
This story is reminiscent of the old fable,
"The Ant and the Grasshopper," with Raven taking
the role of Grasshopper. Many of the folklore
fables were an object lesson told in a parable, and
"The Raven and the Crow" is no exception.
According to Chief Sampson, tribes felt that the
most important lesson contained in the story was the
warning against yielding to insincere flattery. Of course,
there are several useful truths in the legend, all
of which are still worth heeding today.*

# The Raven and The Crow

When there was only one raven in the world, he lived high on the rocky ledges of the Upper Skagit River country.

The creatures of the forest called him Colkus. He could be seen on warm summer days, flying from rock to stump, watching others work.

Unlike his cousin Crow, Colkus never prepared for the cold winter months. During the fall harvest, he laughed when Crow warned him to follow the example of Squirrel and put aside something for the coming winter.

But now Colkus was not laughing. The winter snows had drifted over the ground, covering all remaining food. Colkus faced starvation unless he could persuade someone to share.

He flew to the dead fir where Squirrel made

her nest. Poking his head in the entrance hole, Colkus saw her huge supply of pine nuts, seeds, and other food.

"I stopped by," he greeted, "because I knew you had more food than you could ever use." He said he was starving and asked for a few pine nuts to help support him until the snow melted.

"You refused to save for winter and scoffed at us for saving," Squirrel scolded. "You deserve to starve. I will not help you."

Colkus winged his way to a cave where Bear was staying. Bear, who slept most of the winter, could not be wakened. Raven looked around his cave and, finding no food, left.

"There must be someone who will invite me to dinner," Colkus thought. "Squirrel refused to help, and Bear is sleeping." Raven sat high in a tree to decide on a plan.

"My cousin Crow will provide me with plenty of food," Colkus chuckled to himself. "She is easily fooled." Raven set his wings and sailed down the mountain to visit Crow.

"Cousin Crow," he called. "We must talk of your coming party."

"I plan no party," Crow replied.

"Will you sing at your party?" Colkus asked.

"Sing?" Crow questioned.

"But you are very talented and possess a beautiful voice. We would be disappointed if you refused to sing," Raven said.

"You like my singing?" Crow asked.

"We love your singing," Colkus assured. "The cold has chilled the forest, and many of us are cold and very hungry. Your singing would help us forget our frozen feet and empty stomachs."

Raven proposed that Crow invite all the animals in the forest to a big feast, and, while they ate, she could entertain them with her singing. Crow, overcome by her cousin's flattery, consented to host the dinner party.

"I will take care of inviting the guests," Colkus volunteered. "You can practice your songs and prepare the food."

*"You like my singing?" Crow asked Colkus.*

Crow, who was noted more for her thriftiness than for her singing voice, had worked very hard to collect all the food she had stored for the winter. While she was preparing the feast, Colkus went out to invite the guests.

He offered an invitation to every animal in the forest, saying, "I am holding a great feast. You must come and join us as I have worked very hard to make it possible.

"We will have fern roots, wild potato, dried berries, fish, and meat," he announced. "My cousin Crow is helping prepare the food for this great occasion and has promised to sing."

At the feast, everyone except Crow ate and ate. Crow, encouraged by the guests, sang song after song. From sunup past sunset and into the night, Crow sang. Her voice grew coarser and coarser until all she could say was "Caw-caw." Understanding what was happening, Deer stopped and prayed for future generations of Crow.

As was the custom of that time, the guests collected the uneaten food and left for their homes. Crow had not only lost her singing voice, but she had not a morsel of food left.

Also according to custom, each guest was obligated to invite the host to a return feast. Since all the guests thought Colkus had furnished the food, he was invited to enough dinners to keep him in food for several winters.

Crow, who had been fooled by her cousin's flattery, never regained her singing voice and was destined to sit by the side of trails, picking up the crumbs dropped by travelers.

# The Boy with the Long Hair

One of the most respected tribal positions a brave could
hold was that of the chief hunter.
In order to retain his title, the holder had to prove
himself when challenged. A series of
competitive tests matched the ability of the
challenger against the skill of the chief hunter.
Often these tests were so severe that one or both men
were killed in attempting to complete them.
The chief hunter carefully watched the young tribal
hunters who might someday challenge his title.
Sometimes he was a cruel man who would plot a young
hunter's early destruction to avoid a showdown later.
This Swinomish legend tells of such a man, and
also indicates how extreme the competition
for the title of chief hunter could be.
"The Boy With the Long Hair" was told, not
sung or chanted. Although it is said to have originated
with Swinomish storytellers, there is evidence that

*it spread to nearly every tribe in the
Puget Sound country and even to some on the
southern tip of Vancouver Island.*

# The Boy with the Long Hair

A young boy was born who was said to possess a special hunting ability given him by the spirit of the wolf. When he began to develop into a great hunter, the old chief hunter started to worry.

"I must get rid of this boy before he challenges me. He can already hunt better than I," the older man thought, and he began to plot the boy's death.

The young hunter, fearing his life might be in danger, decided to search for his guide, the wolf spirit. Early one morning he left his village and hiked deep into the forest.

During the hike the boy noticed that his hair was growing at an unusual rate. Longer and longer it grew until he had to tie it into long braids that hung to his knees.

When dusk settled into darkness, the young hunter was seated on a rock enjoying his warming fire. Suddenly, the flames died down, and he felt a chill come over his body.

"There is no need to be frightened," said a voice from the smoke. "I have come to help you, not harm you.

"You have noticed that your hair has grown much longer," the spirit voice continued. "Under no circumstances are you to cut it."

The voice also told of a dog the size of a mouse living under the rock on which the boy was sitting. "You will catch this small dog and keep it in your hair," the voice ordered. "Someday it may save your life with its magic."

Following the instructions, the boy quickly caught the tiny dog and placed it on his head. Then he wound his braided hair around the top of his head, making a small house for his mouse-sized animal.

Upon returning to the village, many of the

*He wound his braided hair around the top of his head,*
*making a small house for his mouse-sized animal.*

people did not recognize him with his long hair. Others, noticing his transformation, proclaimed him ready, having attained manhood, to challenge the chief hunter.

For weeks the tribe talked of the test between the long-haired boy and the old man to see which of the two would be proclaimed chief of the hunters. It was decided that the rivals should be placed on an island, each armed with one spear. Only one canoe would be left for the hunters. The winning brave would be the one who was first to make a kill and paddle it back to the mainland, since he would then have proven his superiority as a hunter.

Early in the day, the younger man made a fine kill. He had carefully stalked a deer and successfully driven his spear into the animal. Even the finest hunters seldom accomplished this feat.

Fearing the loss of his title, the old hunter ran to the canoe and started paddling for shore, leaving the boy with the long hair stranded on the island without a canoe.

When the old hunter reached the mainland, he called to the evil spirit to produce rain and high water. Rain fell, and the tide came in. The water climbed higher and higher on the island. Soon all the land was covered.

The young hunter faced certain death as the rising sea water swirled about his shoulders. He had given up hope of surviving when a spirit voice called to him from across the water.

"Listen to me. Listen to me. Hear what I have to say," the voice called. "Remember the little dog in your hair."

"How can an animal so small save me from these rising waters?" the boy asked as he removed the dog from his braids. While he was untangling it from his hair, water splashed up and wet the little animal.

Like all dogs with a wet coat, the little animal began to shake the water out of his hair. Each time the dog shook himself, he grew larger. Finally he was the size of a pony. The boy jumped on his back and directed him toward

where his deer had floated off in the tidal current. When he found his prey, he laid it carefully across the dog's back. Then, grasping the huge dog by the tail, he ordered him to swim to shore.

At the village the youth with the long hair was proclaimed chief tribal hunter by his people, who had feared him lost in the high water. The older hunter was stripped of his title and disgraced for his evil acts.

The boy never cut his hair, and with the help of his dog he was the finest tribal hunter the people ever had. The dog helped his master locate game and then hauled it back to the village on his back.

The pair served the tribe for many years, and since they accomplished such fantastic feats while hunting, they were never challenged.

# Medicine Man Tales

*Medicine men were an important part of primitive*
*Indian tribal life. Every tribe had one,*
*if not several, of these people who were thought*
*to be gifted with a guiding spirit that could heal the sick.*
*They were treated with great respect, for the*
*Indians believed they had great spirit strength.*
*When white settlers brought civilization*
*to the Puget Sound country, they were accompanied*
*by medical doctors. The Indians discovered*
*that the white man's medicine was often more successful*
*than that of their own tribal doctors,*
*and medicine men found they were losing the*
*influence and political power they had once held.*
*In an effort to reestablish the importance*
*of tribal medicine, stories of the successes of medicine*
*men were circulated. It was hoped these legends*
*would prolong primitive healing practices.*
*The three stories that make up this chapter were*
*told until the early 1900s.*

# Sam Dan and the Government Doctor

An Indian child was very ill in a government hospital, and the white doctors had all but given up hope for her.

Hearing of this, the tribal medicine man, Sam Dan, went to the hospital. The doctor was not there, so he went to the room of the child and administered his own kind of medicine.

Using the dresser as a tom-tom, Sam Dan gently beat out a rhythm to accompany his healing chant. The government doctor returned just after the child had passed the crisis.

"What are you doing here," he snapped at Sam Dan.

"I am curing my child as it seems that you are not able to do so," the shaman replied.

"What kind of medicine have you given the child?" the white medical doctor asked.

*Using the dresser as a tom-tom, Sam Dan gently beat out a rhythm to accompany his healing chant.*

"I have called upon my guide, the great spirit of the blackfish, to heal this girl," Sam Dan answered. "The spirit has spoken and the child will be well again."

Many years later, an Indian mother brought her child to the medicine man Sam Dan. He looked at the child and took him to a nearby white medical doctor.

"Why have you brought this child to me?" the white doctor asked. "If your medicine is so powerful, why don't you cure him yourself?"

"This boy has white man's sickness, and my medicine will not cure him," the tribal medicine man admitted.

Indians from the Skagit River country tell how Sam Dan's honesty earned him the respect of the white doctor, who introduced him as "Dr. Dan." Until Sam Dan died, white men called him "Dr. Dan" and treated him just the same as any other doctor.

# The Grizzly and the Rattlesnake Men

In the early days of the Washington Territory, the Duwaumish Indian Chief held a big potlatch in the area that is now South Seattle.

During the exchange of gifts, it was noticed that the chief's daughter was very ill. The leading medicine men of the tribes assembled tried to treat the little girl, but her condition steadily declined.

The people believed that the evil spirit had taken complete control of her, and that if she were not successfully cured, the entire potlatch would be cursed, and the tribes would face hardships for years to come.

Finally in desperation, her father called out to all the Indians assembled, "Is there *anyone* who can help my daughter?"

A young brave stepped forward and said he

was from the Upper Skagit tribe. His Indian name was reported to be Yalahotse, but most of the Indians knew him as Dr. Dick because of his healing talents.

Another young man came to the chief and identified himself as a Yakima. Without waiting, the Yakima started to dance and chant, calling to his spirit guide, the rattlesnake.

When the Yakima started his song, Dr. Dick began to sing a strange chant. A huge fire, fed by large logs, seemed to burn bright as the two called on their spirit guides for help.

Then the Yakima Indian danced rapidly three times around the fire, and as he circled the flames, they produced smoke that coiled on the ground, mysteriously taking the shape of a rattlesnake.

The Indians drew back as the snake slowly squirmed in the direction of the sick child, who was lying on a bed of cedar boughs not far away. The rattler worked its way to the girl, and when

*The rattler worked its way to the girl.*

it was only a few inches from her face, it coiled as if it were going to strike.

Dr. Dick, still singing his strange chant, walked to the girl's bed. As the child's heartbeat grew weaker and began to falter, Dr. Dick made a grabbing motion in the direction of her heart.

Almost instantly she began to regain her

color, and in a few hours she was completely well.

Explaining his actions, Dr. Dick told the Indians that his spirit guide, the grizzly bear, had pulled the evil spirit from the girl when it had become terror stricken at the sight of the rattle-snake.

So impressed were the Indians of the Puget Sound area, that they have told this story over and over. A grizzly bear carved in tribute to Dr. Dick for saving the chief's daughter appears on the Swinomish Reservation totem pole.

# The Legend of the Hail

Susan Tiny was small just as her name implied. She was also very quiet.

Because she was so small, many of her Upper Skagit tribesmen believed she possessed a very powerful guiding spirit. Although they often questioned her about it, she always refused to discuss it.

One day when she was about to go out and dig roots with other maidens of the tribe, she was told that one of the men of her tribe was dying. The man had been involved in a serious fight with another Indian and had received deep knife wounds in his chest and stomach. The tribal medicine men had worked on him for days, but his condition only worsened. Now he was close to death.

Susan Tiny stopped by his cabin. Seeing that his condition was grave, she rushed to his bedside and started to sing softly.

*He was walking towards her from the east, and*
*thousands of small hail pellets were falling*
*on him from a clear sky.*

Her song told of how she received her spirit
medicine. She sang of a seven-day fast when she
was very young. On the seventh day of her fast,
she walked deep into the forest until she met a

stranger. He was walking towards her from the east, and thousands of small hail pellets were falling on him from a clear sky.

He stopped and talked, the song continued, and as he spoke, hail fell around them although the sun was shining brightly. Susan Tiny learned she would have a long and happy life. She also learned that whenever she wanted powerful medicine for helping herself or others, she was to call upon the hail.

As she sang, the Indians standing around the injured brave's bed saw strength flow from the song into his body. By the end of her song he was able to sit up, and a few hours later he was entirely well.

# The Legend of Pathasos

*The story of Pathasos, the young giant who was
deceived by evil magic in his quest for
the title of chief hunter, is one of the oldest in this book.
It was told in a chant accompanied by a dance and
was common to most of the northern Puget
Sound tribes. This legend was presented by
children during potlatches, but when
potlatches were banned, it almost faded into extinction.
Chief Sampson is one of only a handful
who can recall the chant that told this story.
Many longhouses, long since decayed and burned in
land-clearing fires, had this legend carved in
their supporting pillars.*

# The Legend of Pathasos

Pathasos was a young boy who stood taller than the tallest men in his village. He could run faster, shoot an arrow straighter, and perform more feats of strength than many of his elders.

"Pathasos will make a fine hunter chief someday," the men of his tribe would say. Everyone agreed but old Thsar.

Thsar held the title of chief tribal hunter and did not want to lose it. Each day, he could see, the boy was gaining in popularity, and the old hunter grew more and more jealous.

"Have I not always led our hunters to the kill?" the old chief would ask his tribesmen. "Is not my arrow true and my harpoon accurate?"

"But the boy grows larger with each setting of the sun," the people would answer. "Surely he possesses a spirit guide of great power."

After many months the older hunter could stand it no longer and began to plot against the youthful giant. "The boy has grown taller than two men and has the strength of four," Thsar told himself. "He will soon be able to replace me."

How to dispose of the boy without arousing the anger of the tribe filled the thoughts of the old chief. Pathasos had become very popular with the people and to kill him openly would bring Thsar immediate reprisal.

So Thsar took his problem to his uncle, who was a medicine man wise in the ways of evil magic. They talked far into the night, and finally they arrived at a plan.

They would carve a hair seal from cedar and fill it with evil spirits. Anyone who harpooned the wooden animal would bring it to life and be swept away to the Far North. The spirits would give the seal enough strength to pull the largest canoe far beyond the sight of a sharp-eyed brave.

"Before the sun rises, we must finish the carving or it will not accept the spirits," the medicine man warned. The men worked by the light of a warming fire. As the flames projected their shadows onto the wall of the hut, they carefully carved lifelike detail into the cedar seal.

The sun had not yet risen when Thsar and the medicine man took the carving to the beach. Dancing a powerful medicine ceremony, they filled the seal with evil magic. Then they pushed it into the outgoing tide and chanted:

"Over the waves, to the North you'll go
And deliver Pathasos to the Eskimos."

Returning to the village, they announced that a seal had been sighted off the beach.

"Let us see what a great hunter Pathasos is," Thsar taunted. "Is he man enough to kill a small seal without help?"

"I will go after the seal," the young brave answered. "I will make the kill without help."

As Pathasos stalked the seal, crouching low in

his canoe, the people lined the beach to watch the boy show off his skill. He quietly maneuvered into position and drove his bone-tipped harpoon into the lifelike carving.

As the tip of the harpoon pierced the wood, the evil spirits stored in it came to life. The seal started to swim north, towing Pathasos behind him. The boy, although nearly twice the size of a grown man, could not free his hands from the harpoon handle.

The people were disappointed that Pathasos could not pull in the seal. They did not know it had been filled with evil magic.

"He could never match my ability," Thsar told the people. "You just saw for yourself."

The cedar seal towed Pathasos north past the land of the hostile Duck tribe. When he was finally able to free his hands from the harpoon, he was off the shore of the Eskimos.

Pathasos was greeted on the beach by some Eskimo warriors, who found the boy to be friendly despite his great size.

Explaining that a hostile Duck tribe raided their village regularly, taking women and children as slaves, the Eskimos enlisted the boy's help in defending their homes.

Early the next morning, the Ducks attacked. But because of Pathasos's great size and strength, he was able to destroy the raiding party single-handed. Then he formed a war party of Eskimos and led them south to the main village of the hostile Duck tribe.

Pathasos and the Eskimos attacked, and after a fierce battle, defeated the Ducks.

The Eskimos were now assured of living in peace. "You are truly our great leader," they told Pathasos and invited him to stay with them forever.

But Pathasos declined, stating, "I have been disgraced before my people, and I must return to prove my ability." When he explained how he had been the victim of an evil spirit, the Eskimos promised to help him return to his tribe.

They filled his canoe with food, skins, and

*Pathasos formed a war party of Eskimos.*

other supplies for the long trip. A party volunteered to escort Pathasos south along the coastline.

After a week of travel, the group spotted a bank of dense fog ahead. The Eskimos decided to return to the North, leaving Pathasos supplies and information on how to return to his land.

As the young giant paddled through the fog, he stopped frequently to hurl his huge harpoon at the shoreline. Each time it struck land, it caused a landslide, and the Indians claim this is why the coastline from Alaska to Puget Sound is so irregular.

Pathasos eventually found his way back to his people. Upon seeing the young man return, the old chief Thsar fled with his evil uncle to a tribe in southern Puget Sound. Pathasos claimed the title of chief tribal hunter and became the greatest hunter ever to hunt game in all the Skagit country

# The Legends of the Mink

*Puget Sound Indians loved to tell stories*
*about the animals that roamed their lands, but*
*none were more popular than those about the mink.*
*The mink was usually described as a*
*braggart in the legends, just as he is in "The Mink and*
*the Weasel" and "The Mink and the Sun."*
*These two stories are said to come from the series*
*of fables told by the star child to the Puget Sound*
*Indians. The star child always combined*
*his stories with a moral lesson because he wanted to*
*instruct the Indians in the proper way to behave.*
*Because the early Indians believed so strongly in the*
*teachings of the star child, Christian*
*missionaries, arriving in the early 1830s, found*
*it easy to convert the Indians to Christianity.*
*Originally, there were many star child legends, but*
*all except the two told here have passed on*
*with the people who told them. These stories, always*
*narrated without music or dancing, were*
*common with most of the Puget Sound tribes.*

*According to tribesmen, both the mink and the weasel
had cunning and magic, but while the
latter worked within his known capabilities, the
former was always attempting to exceed
his. Ordinarily, it was the weasel who helped the mink
back to his feet after he fell short of his goal.
But in "The Mink and the Sun" there is no
weasel to help the impudent Mink.*

# The Mink and the Weasel

One afternoon Mink was boasting that he could perform more magic than anyone or anything in the entire world.

"You certainly are not trying to say that you can do as much magic as the great spirit one?" his cousin Weasel asked.

"I am the greatest magician in the entire world," Mink answered. "That includes everything."

The great spirit heard every word Mink said and vowed he would play a trick on Mink at the first opportunity.

One day Mink caught a large salmon, which was very tiring work. He placed the salmon over a beach fire, and while it was roasting, he dozed off to sleep.

"This is what I've been waiting for," the

great spirit said as he quietly walked up to the sleeping animal. "I shall play a trick on him that he will never forget."

After eating Mink's salmon, the spirit rubbed fish oil around the sleeping animal's mouth. Then he smeared salmon over Mink's paws and placed the salmon bones beside him.

"This should fool him," the spirit said and slipped into a hiding place to watch the fun when Mink awakened.

Some time later Mink opened his eyes to discover his salmon had been eaten to the bones. Then he tasted the oil around his mouth and saw the salmon meat on his paws.

"How can I eat a salmon without my stomach knowing it?" Mink asked himself. "There's fish oil all around my mouth, and salmon flesh smeared over my paws. Yet my stomach feels empty. This is most puzzling."

"Puzzling for you, Mink, but not for me," the spirit said, holding his sides with laughter. "I ate

your salmon, but rubbed the oil on your mouth and put the flesh on your hands to make you think you had eaten it," the spirit confessed. "Do you still think you are the world's greatest magician?" the great spirit asked.

"Oh yes," replied Mink.

"Then I shall give you one last chance to prove your worth," he told Mink ."But," he warned, "if you fail to follow my instructions, you will die."

Mink agreed to the contest and was given two blocks of wood. He was then directed to a nearby stream.

"Walk along the water's edge while striking the wood together," the spirit instructed. "If the shoreline is uneven, and difficult to follow, you still must walk along the water's edge the entire distance. It will take quite a trick to do this, but if you fail, it will cost you your life."

Mink hiked downstream along the water's edge, striking the pieces of wood together. For

the first few hours he followed the spirit's instructions, but the travel was difficult, and Mink became tired.

When Mink came to a sand spit that jutted out into the current, he thought how much easier it would be to shortcut across the spit rather than follow the water's edge. "I could run across in ten steps and no one would ever know," he thought to himself.

He looked upstream to see if anyone had followed him. Then he looked downstream. Seeing no one, he started to dash across the sand spit, hoping to play a trick on the great spirit.

After he took two steps, a bolt of lightning shot from the sky and struck him dead. The bones and skin of the animal were separated by the impact, and it seemed that all future generations of Mink were doomed.

Weasel discovered his cousin's remains, and carefully collecting all the pieces, he moulded Mink into a figure much like his own. Then

*Mink slowly rose to his feet and said,*
*"I must have been asleep for a long time. I feel so weak."*

Weasel was ready to use his magic medicine power on Mink. He danced around Mink's re-shaped body and called to the spirit to restore his cousin's life.

Finally Mink rubbed his eyes. Slowly rising to his feet he said, "I must have been asleep for a long time. I feel so weak."

"You were not asleep. I found you lying on this sand spit dead," Weasel replied.

Mink ran to the water and studied his reflection. "I look different. I look like you, Weasel," he complained.

"I reshaped you that way after I found you in pieces," Weasel explained. "You were struck by lightning because you disobeyed the great spirit."

Mink then tried to make some of his magic, but found his talents had disappeared. "What will I do?" he asked. "I look like a large weasel and have no magical power."

"It will serve as a punishment to you for dis-

obeying the instructions of the great spirit," Weasel answered. "I still have my power, and each winter I shall turn myself white to remind you of your mistakes."

Many years have passed, but each winter the color of the weasel's coat changes to white. Indians say that this is a sign from the spirits that the laws must be obeyed.

# The Mink and the Sun

Near the beginning of time, Puget Sound Indians say, Mink set out to try and outsmart all the tribes living on earth at that time.

One by one, the Indian peoples fell victim to the mischievous Mink. After he had played a trick on the last tribe, he looked to the heavens and decided that Sun and Moon were no smarter than he.

"I must go up and visit them for I want an easy job like lighting the world," Mink thought to himself. So he climbed the tree to the stars, and followed the planets until he came to the home of Sun.

Sun was away from home, hard at work lighting the world, when Mink called, but Sun's squaw let him in because he told her he was a relative of her husband. When Sun came home

and learned of Mink's presence, he decided to punish him for his deception.

"Mink loves to play jokes of this sort upon people," Sun explained to his wife. "We will surprise him with a joke of our own."

The next morning he dressed Mink in a shining suit and presented him with a walking stick and a torch. "You claim that providing light for the earth is an easy job," Sun said. "Then go out and light the world. All you have to do is walk across the sky and direct your light to shine on the world below."

"I knew that all the time," Mink snapped back. "But I really don't need such a long walking stick. Is there any reason you carry it?"

"You look so distinguished carrying a walking stick," Sun replied. "You had better carry it because I'm sure you'll find some use for it along the way."

What Sun did not tell Mink was that the stick was used to vault the Milky Way. "If

Mink is as smart as he thinks, he'll discover how to use the stick without my explanation," Sun told his squaw after Mink had left.

Mink found that the job of lighting the world was more difficult than he thought. The shiny suit Sun had given him was heavy and very tiring to wear. And his torch was heavy, for it was filled with enough pitch to last the entire day.

By the time Mink reached the Milky Way he was tired and discouraged. Walking up and down the banks of the Milky Way, he found it too wide to jump and too swift to wade.

"How can I jump across this river of stars with a torch and this long stick," Mink reasoned. "It will be hard enough to make the jump carrying this torch," he thought. "The only reason Sun gave me the stick was to make me fail."

So the little animal threw the walking stick far out into the current of the Milky Way.

Exploring the banks of the river of stars,

*Over and over Mink tumbled down the Milky Way.*

Mink found what appeared to be a narrow spot in the Milky Way. Although the opposite bank seemed close, the current was very swift.

"This must be the place to cross," Mink assured himself as he prepared to jump. He backed up, then ran at the river with all the energy he had left in his body. As he neared the bank, he jumped, using his remaining strength. But he fell far short of making it to the other side.

Mink's torch was extinguished, and his shiny suit was darkened by the Milky Way. Over and over he tumbled until carried by the current, he was back on earth.

Until Sun could light another torch to brighten the earth, the world below was thrown into total darkness by Mink's folly. And this was the first eclipse.

The Indians say that the sun occasionally causes another eclipse in order to remind the creatures of the earth that they cannot take the place of any of the heavenly bodies.

# Other Books of Indian Legends

*Sketco, the Raven,* by Robert Ayre. New York: St. Martins, 1962.

*John Rattling-Gourd of Big Cove; A Collection of Cherokee Indian Legends,* by Corydon Bell. New York: Macmillan, 1955.

*Down from the Lonely Mountain; California Indian Tales,* by Jane Curry. New York: Harcourt, Brace & World, 1965.

*Stories California Indians Told,* by Anne B. Fisher. Berkeley: Parnassus, 1957.

*Once Upon a Totem,* by Christie Harris. New York: Atheneum, 1963.

*Indian Tales of the Desert People,* by William D. Hayes. New York: McKay, 1957.

*Badger, the Mischief Maker,* by Kay Hill. New York: Dodd, Mead & Co., 1965.

*Glooscap and His Magic,* by Kay Hill. New York: Dodd, Mead & Co., 1963.

*The World of Manabozho; Tales of the Chippewa Indians,* by Thomas Leekley. New York: Vanguard Press, 1965.

*Nine Tales of Coyote,* by Frances Martin. New York: Harper, 1950.

*Nine Tales of Raven,* by Frances Martin. New York: Harper, 1951.

*Tales of the Cheyennes,* by Grace Jackson Penney. Boston: Houghton Mifflin, 1953.

*Tales of Nanabozho,* by Dorothy N. Reid. New York: Walck, 1963.

*Dancing Horses of Acoma and Other Acoma Indian Stories,* by Helen Rushmore and W. Hunt. Cleveland: World, 1963.

*Cherokee Animal Tales,* by George Scheer. New York: Holiday House, 1968.